ON THE LINE

What's the highest total you can get by drawing a single straight line through this box? Teri drew a line worth 12. Can you do better?

on page 46

7	4	2
3	5	6
9	1	8

Illustration: Vilma Ortiz-Dillon

Answer on page 48

ALLEY-OOPS

Each of these clocks shows a time between noon and midnight. Arrange the times in order, starting from the earliest to the latest.

A

T

M

I

S

I

Once you have the order, write the letters near each clock into the blanks to answer the riddle.

E

I

N

E

H

R

S

P

Illustration: Jerry Zimmerman

When did the bowler like to practice?

____ ____   ____ ____ ____

____ ____ ____ ____ ____   ____ ____ ____ ____

Answer on page 48

CONNECTIONS

Place each number from 1 to 9 onto an engine so that the two connecting engines add up to the number on the engine above it. For example, 1 + 5 = 6 and 5 + 4 = 9.

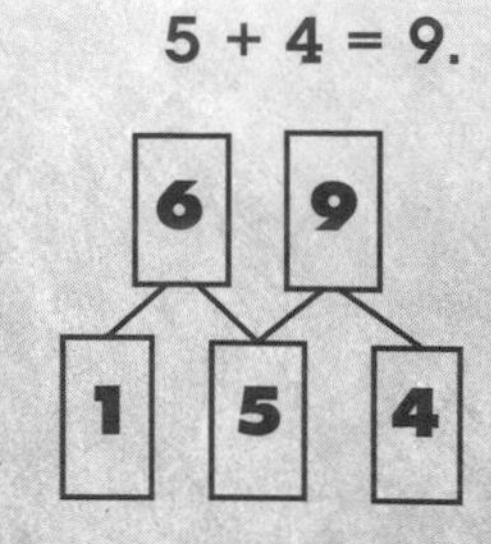

The number 3 is already in place.

12
16
17
3

Illustration: Rick Geary

Answer on page 48

COUNT DOWN

The driver for the Eiderdown Feather Company has been making deliveries all day. He started out with 1,000 pounds of feathers. Can you tell how much he has left to deliver at his last stop?

Hint on page 46

Answer on page 48

Cooter's Coats

Swan Sleep Sacks
203 Pounds

Bird's Bunk Beds
177 Pounds

Elephant Comforters
261 Pounds

Drowsy Duckling Pillows
74 Pounds

Cooter's Coats
____ Pounds
Last Stop

Goosey Gander's Quilts
128 Pounds

Illustration: Scott Peck

PAGE COUNT

The students of Lakeside School are having a contest to see who can read the most pages in one month.

STUDENTS	BOOK PAGES	TOTAL
Corey	100, 124, 200, 150	
Madison	121, 200, 138, 128	
Abu	113, 213, 133, 131	
Sarah	121, 232, 200, 75	
Tanikwa	212, 56, 190, 133	
José	302, 65, 142, 112	
Jamahl	49, 265, 116, 187	
Morgan	300, 121, 132, 88	
Chan	147, 125, 98, 140	
Edward	75, 300, 80, 149	

Can you help the teacher add up the book pages and find the winner from the top ten students?

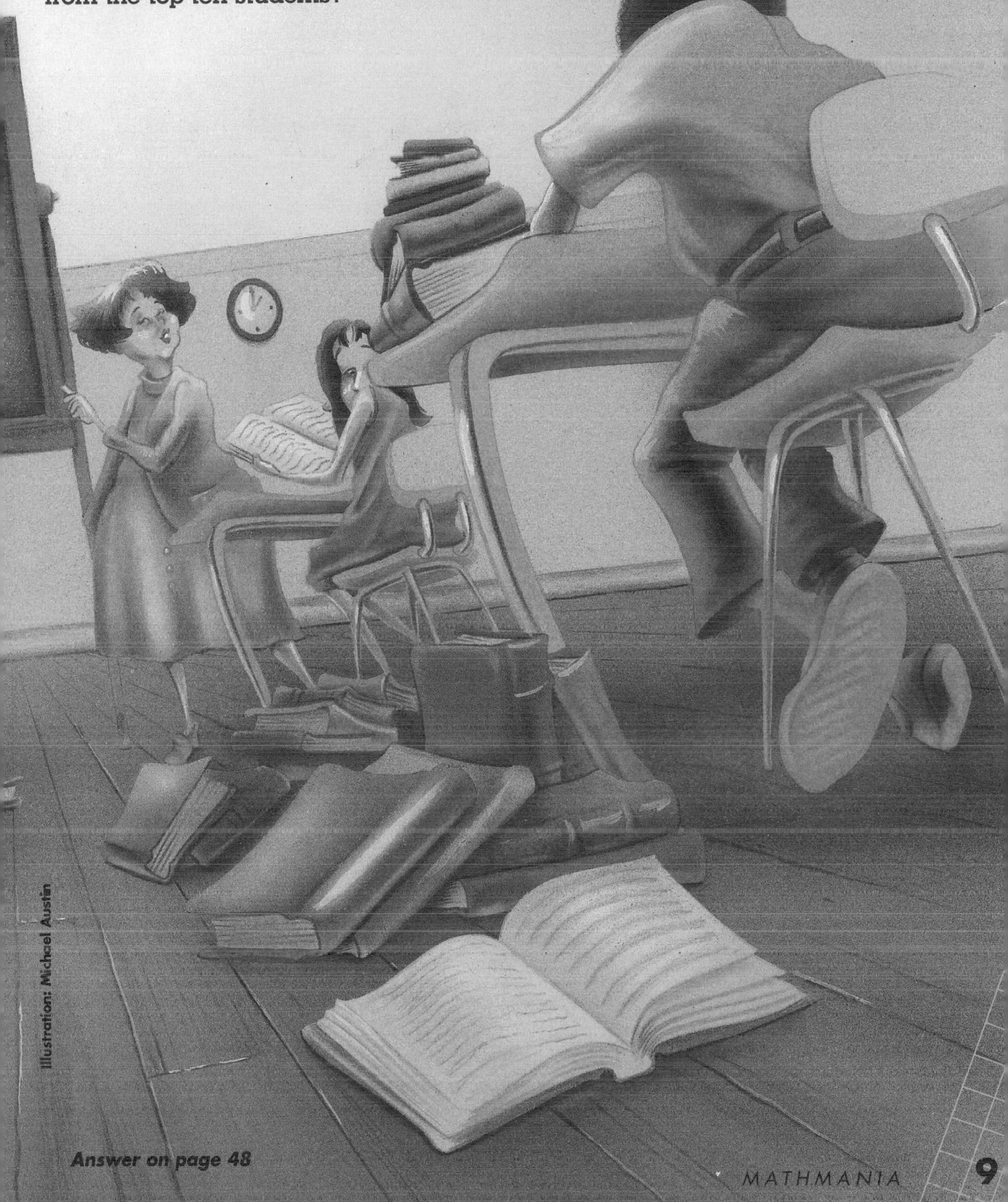

Illustration: Michael Austin

Answer on page 48

SPOTTED SUMS

On Monday, Sharona spotted 5 swallows. Each day since then, the number of swallows she has seen has doubled. On what day of the week will Sharona spot more than 600 swallows?

Week 1		Week 2	
Monday	5	Monday	____
Tuesday	____	Tuesday	____
Wednesday	____	Wednesday	____
Thursday	____	Thursday	____
Friday	____	Friday	____
Saturday	____	Saturday	____
Sunday	____	Sunday	____

Answer on page 48

Hint on page 46

Illustration: David Helton

DOTS A LOT

For a new spin on dot puzzles, find the answer to the problem beside each dot. Work each problem from left to right. Then use a ruler or straightedge to join each set of three dots that has the same answer.

7 × 3 × 1

103 – 83

1 + 2 + 3 + 4 + 5 + 6

1 + 3 + 5 + 7

9 × 5 ÷ 3

212 – 197

3 × 3 × 2

24 + 38 – 44

5 × 2 × 2

240 ÷ 10 – 4

150 – 129

2 × 2 × 2 × 2

83 – 65

1 + 2 + 3 + 4 + 5

32 ÷ 4 × 2

Hint on page 46

Answer on page 48

STACKING STANLEY

Stan is setting up some super stacks. Can you figure out the pattern for each set of stacks and

Illustration: R. Michael Palan

then draw the items that should go in the next two stacks?

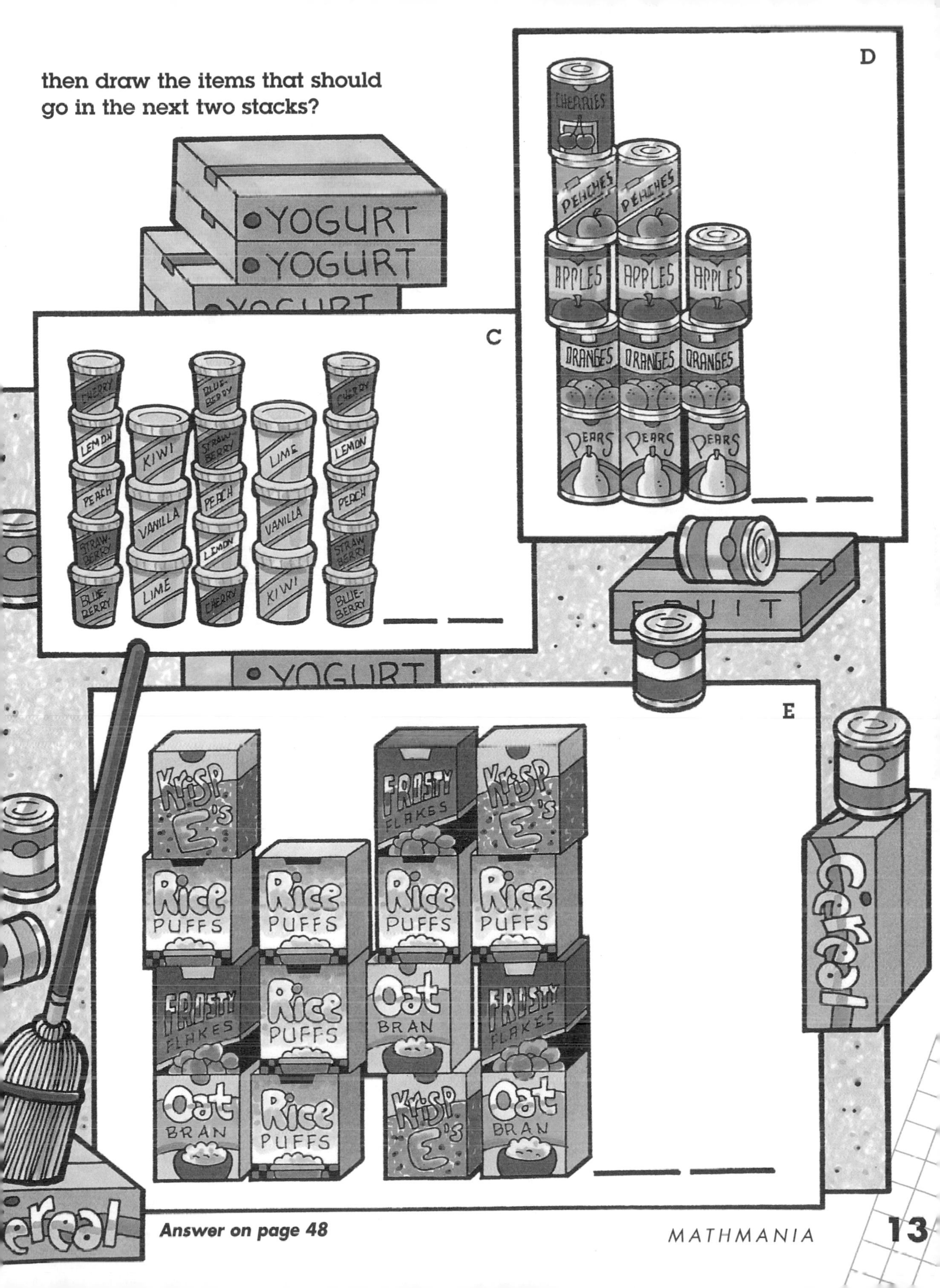

Answer on page 48

CASTLE CALCULATIONS

Each symbol on this scroll serves as a number and a letter. To figure out the number for each, work the math problems. Then put the letter that is beneath each symbol into the blank that matches the number. For example, the helmet stands for the letter *I*. The helmet is also used as the number 1 in the problems.

1. I + I = N
2. N x N = G
3. C − G = G
4. K + K = T
5. L − O = I
6. N x H = L
7. C + N = L
8. S − T = I

Illustration: Michael Austin

Where did King Arthur learn to use his lance a lot?

__ __   __ __ __ __ __ __   __ __ __ __ __ __
1 2   3 2 1 4 5 6   7 8 5 9 9 10

Answer on page 49

SUM SUIT

Kate just got her first job. Now she needs to order some business clothes. She wants to buy a three-piece suit consisting of a jacket, a skirt, and a vest. How much is each piece individually, and how much will she pay altogether?

Illustration: Bill Colrus

Hint on page 46

Answer on page 49

PARTY PUZZLE

Tomas and Tanya are twins. They were born in July on Independence Day. Since there were so many other things going on that same day,

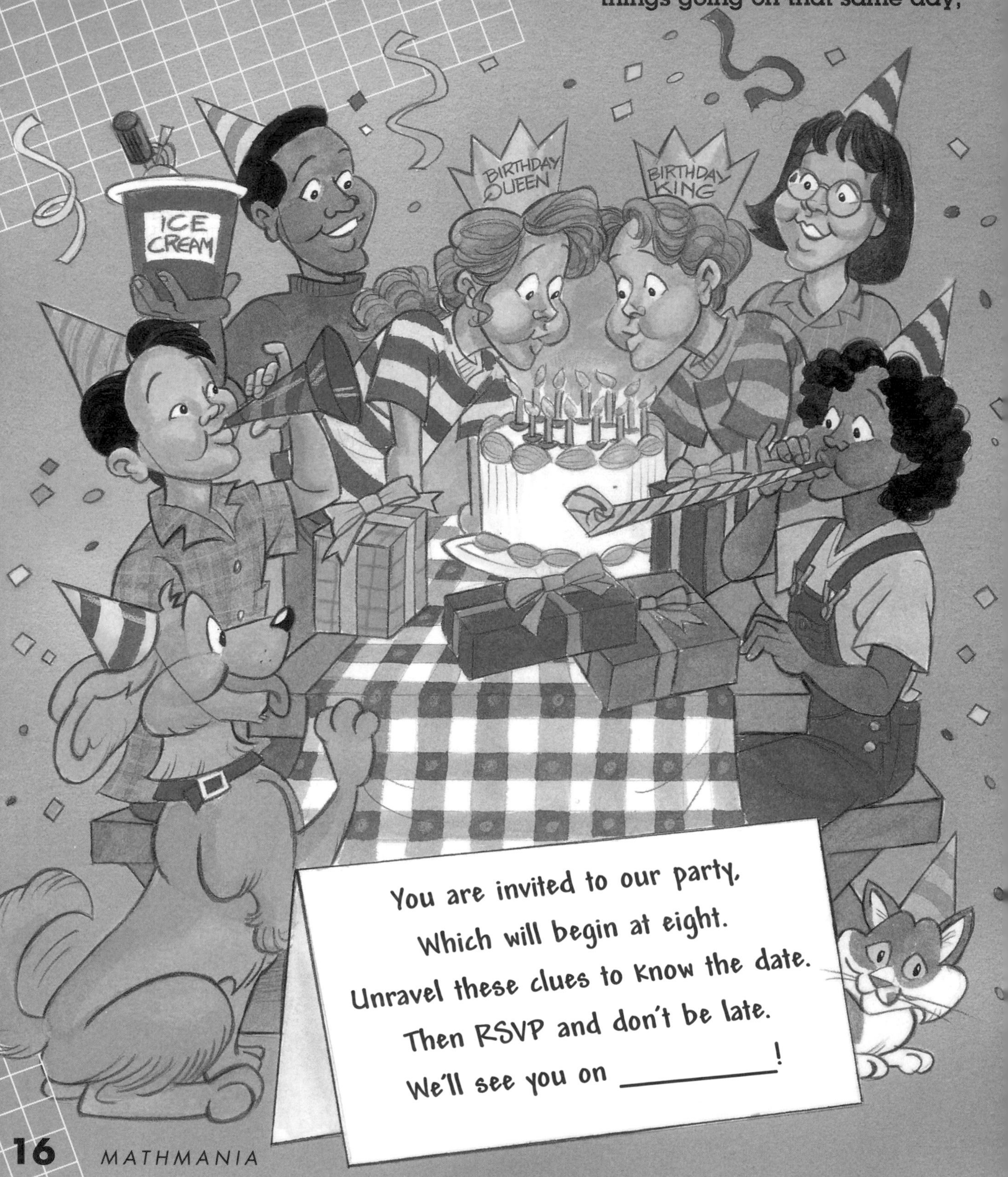
ICE CREAM
BIRTHDAY QUEEN
BIRTHDAY KING
You are invited to our party,
Which will begin at eight.
Unravel these clues to know the date.
Then RSVP and don't be late.
We'll see you on ____________!

they wanted to have their party on a different date. Can you read their invitation and use the calendar to figure out the date of the party?

SUNDAY	MONDAY	TUESDAY	WEDNESDAY	THURSDAY	FRIDAY	SATURDAY
	1	2	3	4	5	6
7	8	9	10	11	12	13
14	15	16	17	18	19	20
21	22	23	24	25	26	27
28	29	30	31			

1. The party is not on a Saturday.
2. It does not fall on a date that corresponds with these dates in other months: Washington's Birthday, Christmas, or Groundhog Day.
3. It's not in the last week of the month.
4. It's not on a Friday.
5. It's not on an odd-number date.
6. It's not on a date that can be evenly divided by 7, 8, or 9.

Illustration: Rocky Fuller

Hint on page 46

Answer on page 49

TRICKY QUICKIES

Watch out for these!

A. Add five lines to these six lines to get nine.

| | | | | |

B. What number is worth more when added than when multiplied?

Answer on page 49

Hint on page 46

Illustration: Jerry Zimmerman

SAND ART

Can you draw this figure without doubling back or crossing over any lines?

Answer on page 49

Illustration: Barbara Gray

SCRAMBLED PICTURE

Copy these mixed-up rectangles onto the next page to unscramble the scene. The letters and numbers

tell you where each rectangle belongs. The first one, A-3, has been done for you.

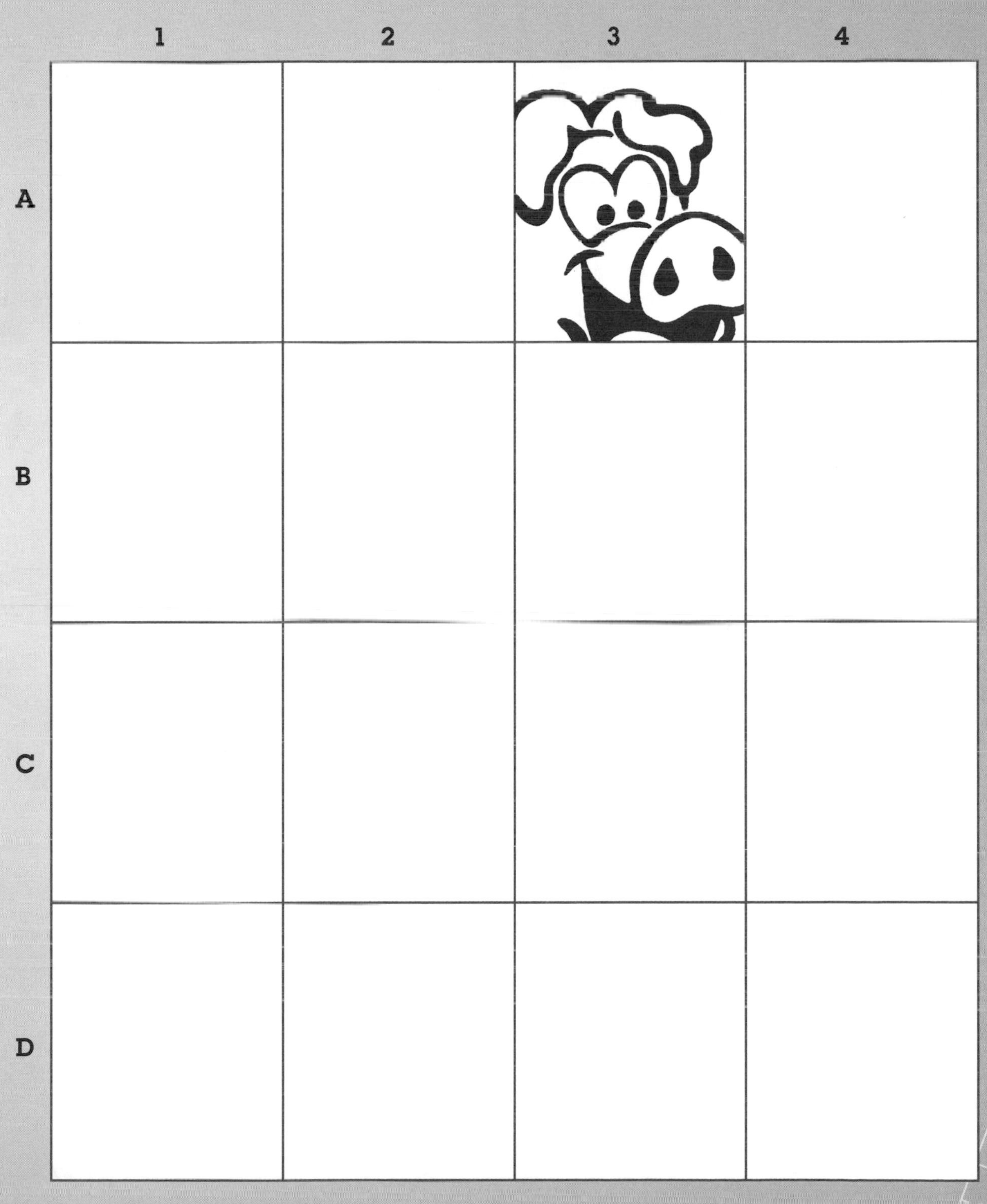

Illustration: Rob Sepanak

Answer on page 49

WHO AM I?

What number is described in each set of statements?

1. I'm a two-digit number. If you add or multiply my digits, the answer will be the same. If you subtract my digits, the answer is 0. Who am I?

2. I'm a two-digit number. The sum of my digits is 6. My ones digit equals my tens digit. Who am I?

3. I'm a two-digit number less than 20. I equal the same whether I'm read forward or backward. Who am I?

4. I'm a three-digit number. All my digits are even and equal 6 when added together. Who am I?

5. I'm a three-digit number. My ones digit is double my tens digit. My tens digit is double my hundreds. None of my numbers is greater than 5. Who am I?

6. I'm a three-digit number. Added together, my digits equal 1. Who am I?

7. I'm a three-digit number. My digits are all the same and when added together equal 12. Who am I?

8. I'm a five-digit number. All my digits are odd, and each digit is greater than the one on its right.

Answer on page 49

Illustration: Jim Paillot

SUBTRACTION SEQUENCES

Answer the problems, then match the letters to the corresponding numbers in sequence below.

31 − 25	C
23 − 19	T
15 − 13	E
43 − 34	E
11 − 10	T
19 − 16	N
27 − 22	I
35 − 28	K
39 − 31	L
47 − 37	S

Illustration: Jerry Zimmerman

Why did the octopus always laugh at the number after nine?

__ __ __   __ __ __ __ __ __ __

1 2 3   4 5 6 7 8 9 10

Answer on page 49

DIGIT DOES IT

Inspector Digit just received a package of items from an investigator working on a postal forgery case. Unfortunately,

a breeze blew everything off the Inspector's desk. You can help recover the evidence if you decipher the investigator's message.

Illustration: John Nez

Answer on page 49

CERTAIN CIRCLES

Javier and Ramona made a chart of the kids in their school. They put the kids into five different categories as shown on the diagram. Now they must

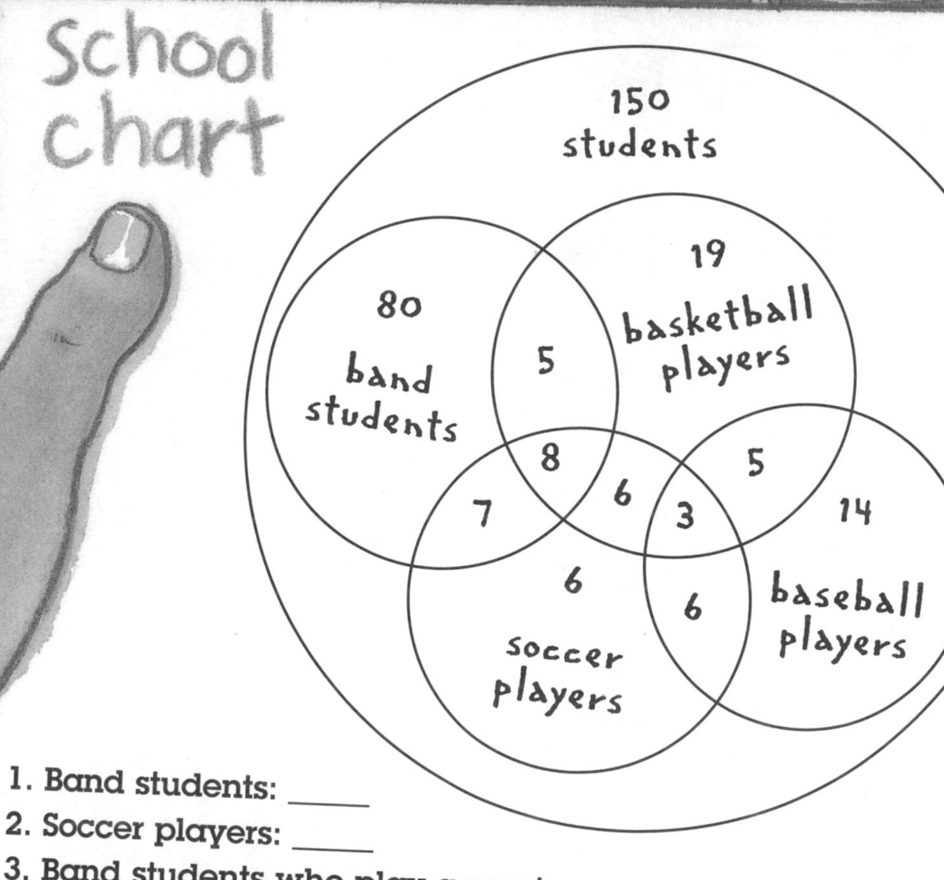

1. Band students: _____
2. Soccer players: _____
3. Band students who play a sport: _____
4. Students who play one sport: _____
5. Students who play two sports: _____
6. Students who play three sports: _____
7. Number of baseball players who are in band: _____
8. Total number of all elementary-school students: _____

tally up the kids for their final report. Use the information on the chart to fill in the proper number of students for each category.

Illustration: Anni Matsick

Ramona liked the circles so much that she made a chart just for the kids on the street where she and Javier live. Can you answer her questions, too?

Lincoln Avenue chart

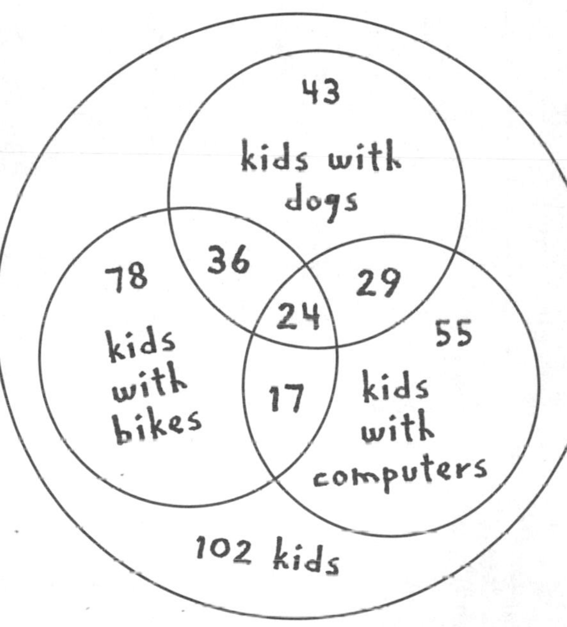

1. Total number of kids who live on Lincoln Avenue:____
2. Kids with dogs:____
3. Kids with bikes:____
4. Kids with both dogs and computers: ____
5. Kids who don't have a dog, a bicycle, or a computer: ____
6. Kids who have a dog, a bicycle, or a computer: ____

Answer on page 49

MATHMAGIC

Illustration: Marc Nadel

EQUAL TIME

Fill in each circle with one of the mathematical signs (+, –, x, ÷) to make each statement equal.

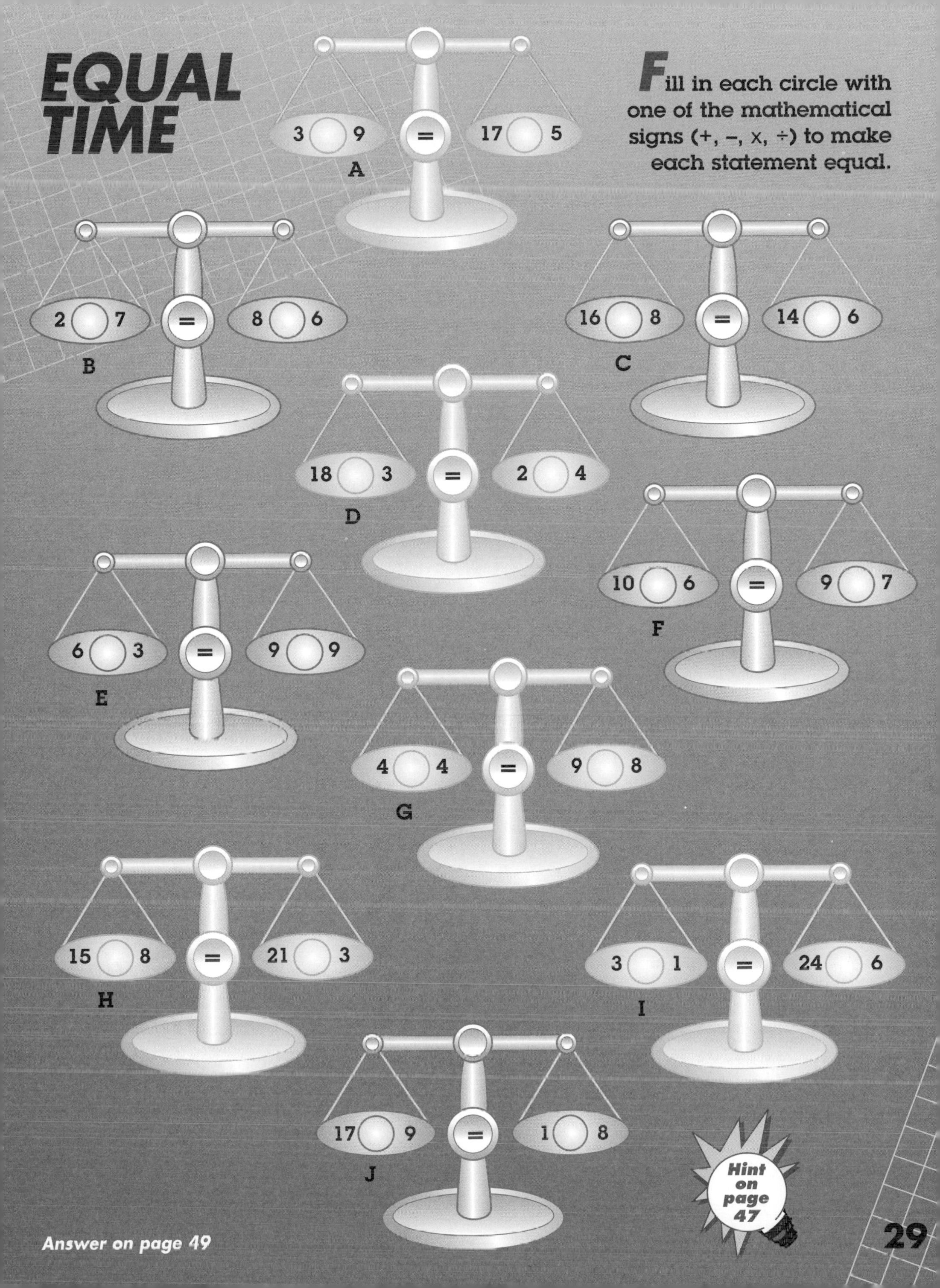

Answer on page 49

HOWDY, PARTNERS!

At the big Mathematics Club Charity Dance-a-thon, each girl on the red team is paired with a boy on the blue team. The blue partner is someone whose numbers equal the numbers on a red shirt in some way. The dancers used addition, subtraction, multiplication, or division to find a partner. For example, the red dancer with shirt 55 is partnered with the blue 25 because $5 \times 5 = 25$. We'll get this dance going once everyone finds a partner.

Illustration: R. Michael Palan

Answer on page 50

BUS BUDDIES

Everyone who lives more than a mile from Sunnydale School can ride the bus. Use the map key to help Driver Dan mark off all the houses of those students who need a ride. Start counting the distance where a dot begins a line.

SHANIECE

CHELSEA

ZOO

LOUIS

SCHOOL

LEO

PARK

TOM

DREW

HECTOR

AMBER

MEGAN

$\frac{1}{8}$ mile

Answer on page 50

Illustration: Diana Zourelias

MEASURE UP

At Melinda's Mansion of Discount Measurement, a big sale on imperfect rulers is underway. But Emma knows a bargain when she sees one. Even with the ruler shown, she can still measure every inch from 1 to 12 without adding or subtracting anything. Can you list how she could do it?

2 3 8 9 11

Hint on page 47

Answer on page 50

Illustration: Don Robison

PAPER PUNCH

The papers on the left were all folded in half or in quarters. Then they were punched as shown.

Illustration: Vilma Ortiz-Dillon

A

B

C

D

Fold

G

E

F

H

Can you match each folded paper with what it looks like unfolded?

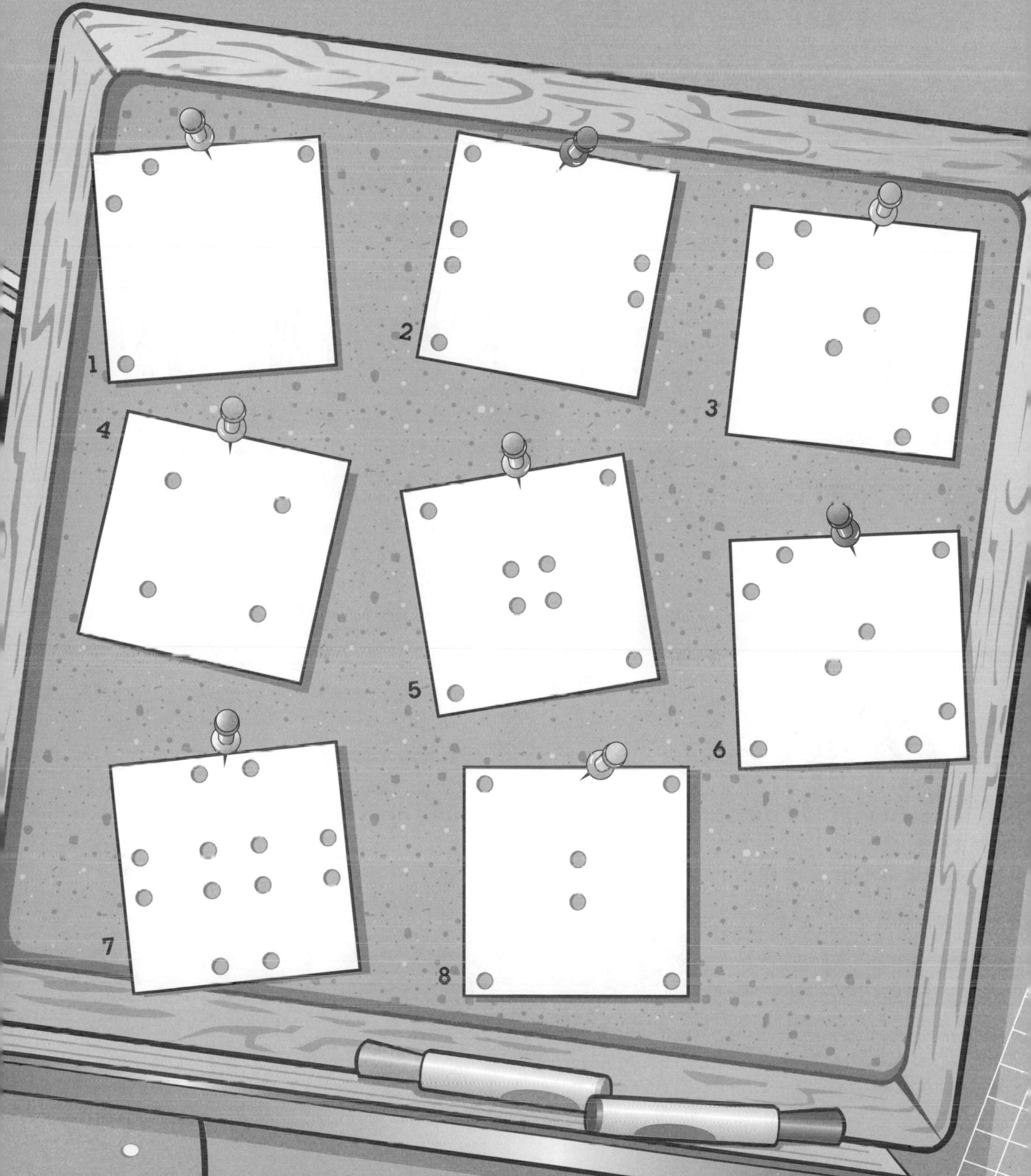

1

2

3

4

5

6

7

8

Answer on page 50

WHAT'S THE DIFFERENCE?

Maria and Mark went shopping last week, but they didn't go together. Each bought the same items at different stores. Figure out the difference between the prices they paid for each item. Who was the better shopper last week?

Illustration: Marc Nadel

Answer on page 50

GETTING AROUND

To spell the name of each method of transportation, connect the letters in the boxes that touch one another either across, up, down, or diagonally. The sum of the values of the letters used must match the number beside each object. Some letters will be used in more than one word, and every letter will be used at least once.

120

151

56

17

1 K	2 C	3 U	4 B	5 U
6 T	7 R	8 A	9 E	10 S
11 O	12 A	13 N	14 A	15 P
16 B	17 X	18 I	19 R	20 L
21 I	22 C	23 Y	24 C	25 E

19

19

45

Hint on page 47

56

Illustration: David Helton

Answer on page 50

SWEET STUFF

At Candy's Confectionery Company, this puzzle is posted on the wall. Anyone who can use the clues to determine the year each candy was first sold gets a free box of chocolates.

Answer on page 50

To use the grid, put an X in the boxes where the information doesn't match and an O where you find the answer.

	1894	1896	1907	1920	1921	1923	1932	1947
Almond Joy								
Baby Ruth								
Cracker Jack								
Hershey Bar								
Hershey's Kisses								
M&M's								
Milky Way								
3 Musketeers								

1. The treat that was sold first was a candy bar.
2. M&M's and Baby Ruth were first sold a year apart.
3. One candy bar has the same number in its name as the decade it was introduced.
4. Almond Joy, Baby Ruth, Hershey's Kisses, and Milky Way were first sold in odd-number years.
5. Milky Way was introduced 27 years after Cracker Jack, which was not the first treat sold, and 24 years before Almond Joy.

Illustration: Scott Peck

Hint on page 47

LIBRARY LAUGHS

Dewey has some funny books in his library. To check one out, solve each problem. Then go to the shelves to find the volume with the number that matches each answer. Put the matching letter in the blank beside each answer. Read down the letters you've filled in to find the title and author of the book Dewey just finished reading.

U 21, N 14, V 22, K 11

F 6, J 10, W 23, A 1, B 2, C 3, D 4, E 5, P 16, Q 17, R 18, S 19, T 20

L 12, M 13, Y 25, G 7, H 8, X 24

Z 26, O 15, I 9

$2 + 4 =$ ____ ____
$17 - 8 =$ ____ ____
$8 \times 3 =$ ____ ____
$18 \div 2 =$ ____ ____
$8 + 6 =$ ____ ____
$9 - 2 =$ ____ ____
$4 \times 1 =$ ____ ____
$40 \div 8 =$ ____ ____
$0 + 5 =$ ____ ____
$21 - 5 =$ ____ ____
$46 \div 2 =$ ____ ____
$24 - 9 =$ ____ ____
$7 \times 3 =$ ____ ____
$20 - 6 =$ ____ ____
$16 \div 4 =$ ____ ____
$19 \times 1 =$ ____ ____
$8 - 6 =$ ____ ____
$5 \times 5 =$ ____ ____
$27 - 8 =$ ____ ____
$3 \times 7 =$ ____ ____
$30 \div 6 =$ ____ ____
$10 - 7 =$ ____ ____
$24 \div 3 =$ ____ ____
$16 - 11 =$ ____ ____
$9 \times 2 =$ ____ ____

Illustration: Scott Peck

Hint on page 47

Answer on page 51

COLOR BY NUMBERS

1 dot—Black
2 dots—Brown
3 dots—Green
4 dots—Blue
5 dots—Gray

Follow the chart to color the shapes.

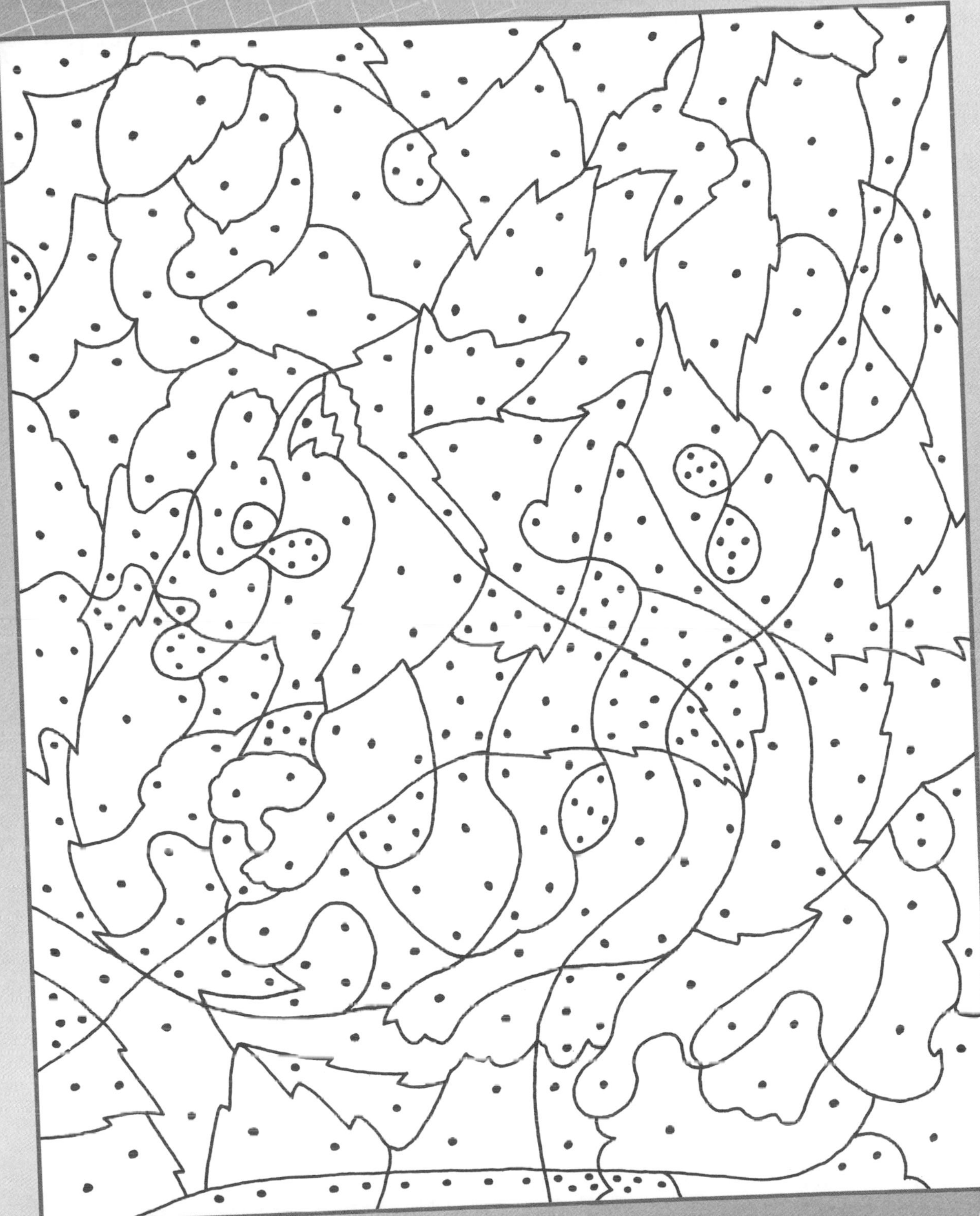

Illustration: Rob Sepanak

Answer on page 51

FIRST CITY

This mystery city was the site of many national firsts. To get here, figure out the year of each event.

D—First U.S. mint to coin money:
1000 + 700 + 90 + 2

L—First U.S. zoo:
1800 + 70 + 4

I—First stock exchange:
1000 + 700 + 90

A—First bank of the U.S.:
1000 + 700 + 90 + 1

L—First baseball game in which one team scored more than 100 runs:
1000 + 800 + 60 + 5

P—First public library:
1000 + 700 + 30 + 1

Then write the letter in the blank above the matching year.

E—First bifocal glasses made: 1000 + 700 + 50 + 2

H—First volunteer fire-fighting company: 1000 + 700 + 70 + 6

A—First animated motion picture shown to an audience: 1000 + 800 + 70

I—First daily newspaper: 1000 + 700 + 80 + 4

P—First root beer drink: 1000 + 800 + 60 + 6

H—First public demonstration of the telephone: 1000 + 800 + 70 + 6

Illustration: Rick Geary

___ ___ ___ ___ ___ ___ ___ ___ ___ ___ ___ ___

1731 1876 1790 1865 1870 1792 1752 1874 1866 1776 1784 1791

Answer on page 51

FRACTION ACTION

Match the two figures that have the same fraction areas shaded. Each figure has one match.

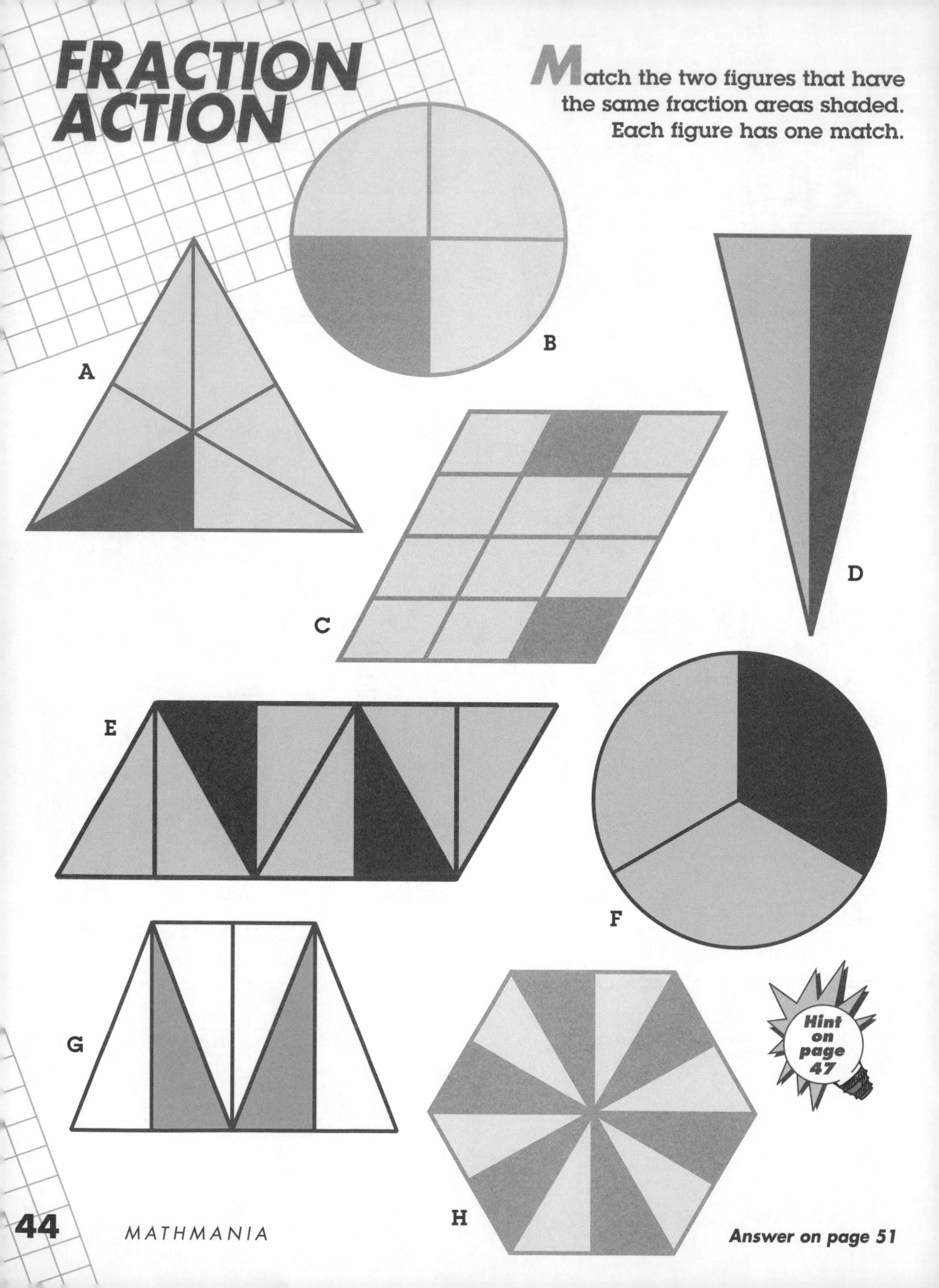

Hint on page 47

Answer on page 51

TINY TOWN

The new city planner knows only the facts on his clipboard. Can you help him figure out the total population of Tiny Town and how many people live on each street?

TINY TOWN
MEENIE AVENUE
EENIE STREET
MYNIE WAY
CHOOSE ROAD
MOE BOULEVARD

$\frac{1}{3}$ of the people on Eenie Street, $\frac{1}{2}$ of the people on Meenie Avenue, $\frac{3}{4}$ of the folks on Mynie Way, $\frac{3}{6}$ of those living on Moe Boulevard, and $\frac{1}{2}$ of the citizens on Choose Road all happen to be the same number, which is 6.

Eenie Street ____
Meenie Avenue ____
Mynie Way ____
Moe Boulevard ____
Choose Road ____
TOTAL POPULATION ____

Answer on page 51

Hint on page 47

Illustration: Bill Colrus

HINTS AND BRIGHT IDEAS

These hints may help with some of the trickier puzzles.

ON THE LINE (page 3)

As in the example, your line does not have to go directly across or up and down.

COUNT DOWN (page 7)

It may help to add up all the deliveries given and then subtract that total from the starting number.

SPOTTED SUMS (page 10)

On Monday, Sharona spotted 5 swallows. On Tuesday she saw 10. On Wednesday she saw 20, and so on.

DOTS A LOT (page 11)

What shape can you form by joining three dots?

STACKING STANLEY (pages 12-13)

Look for clues in both the number of items in each stack and the placement of the items.

SUM SUIT (page 15)

A skirt costs $50.

PARTY PUZZLE (pages 16-17)

Dates that can be divided evenly by 7 are 7, 14, 21, and 28. Washington's Birthday is February 22.

TRICKY QUICKIES (page 18)

For A, *add* does not mean "addition."

DIGIT DOES IT (pages 24-25)

The word *Inspector* appears in the note's greeting. Use the code numbers from this word to help figure out the rest of the message.

CERTAIN CIRCLES (pages 26-27)

Be sure to count all the kids in the different sections of each circle when finding the totals.

EQUAL TIME (page 29)

You may need to do one type of math function on the left side of the equal sign and a different one on the right. For example, 3 + 9 = 17 - 5.

MEASURE UP (page 33)

Use the numbers on the ruler to find the measurements. For example, to get a 1-inch measure, you could use the space between the 2 and 3.

WHAT'S THE DIFFERENCE? (page 36)

Subtract the lower purchase price from the higher for each item.

GETTING AROUND (page 37)

To find BOAT, start in box 16. 16 + 11 + 12 + 6 = 45. Look for CAR beginning in box 2.

SWEET STUFF (pages 38-39)

The newest candy bar, which is not named for a person, was sold 40 years after Hershey's Kisses were introduced.

LIBRARY LAUGHS (page 40)

Remember to consult the books to find the letter that matches each number.

FRACTION ACTION (page 44)

Shape B has 1 out of 4 areas shaded, or $\frac{1}{4}$. Can you find another shape that is $\frac{1}{4}$ shaded?

TINY TOWN (page 45)

6 is equal to $\frac{1}{3}$ of the people on Eenie Street. To find the total number of people living on Eenie Street, multiply 6 by 3.

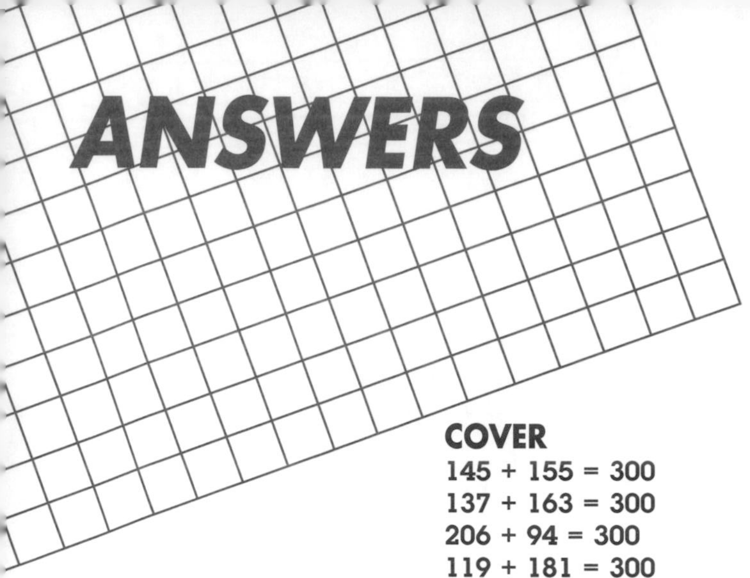

COVER

145 + 155 = 300
137 + 163 = 300
206 + 94 = 300
119 + 181 = 300

ON THE LINE (page 3)

The highest total is 30.

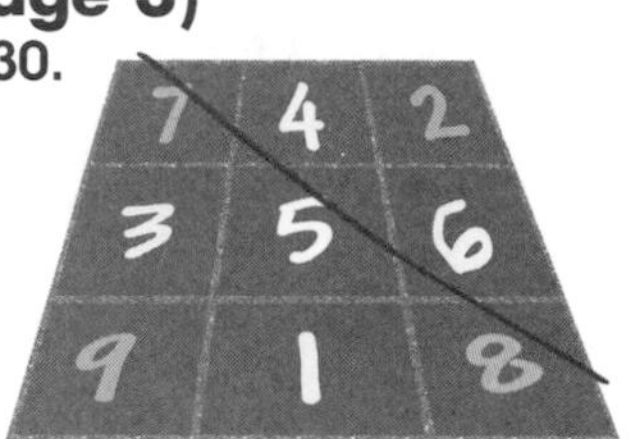

ALLEY-OOPS (pages 4-5)

When did the bowler like to practice?

CONNECTIONS (page 6)

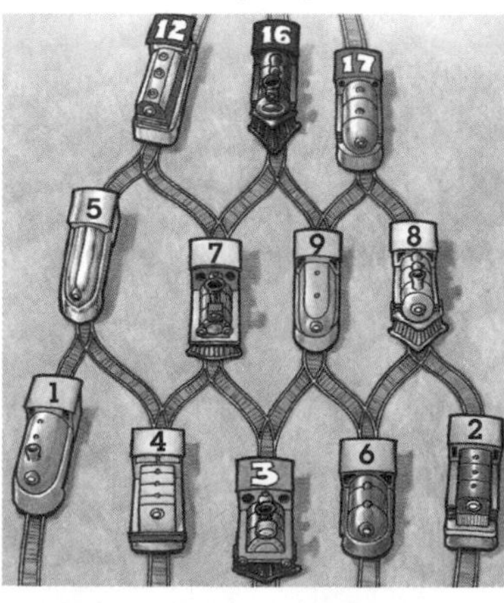

COUNT DOWN (page 7)

The driver dropped off a total of 843 pounds of feathers before arriving at Cooter's Coats. He has 157 pounds left for his last stop.

PAGE COUNT (pages 8-9)

Corey:	100 + 124 + 200 + 150 = 574
Madison:	121 + 200 + 138 + 128 = 587
Abu:	113 + 213 + 133 + 131 = 590
Sarah:	121 + 232 + 200 + 75 = 628
Tanikwa:	212 + 56 + 190 + 133 = 591
José:	302 + 65 + 142 + 112 = 621
Jamahl:	49 + 265 + 116 + 187 = 617
Morgan:	300 + 121 + 132 + 88 = 641
Chan:	147 + 125 + 98 + 140 = 510
Edward:	75 + 300 + 80 + 149 = 604

The winner is Morgan.

SPOTTED SUMS (page 10)

Sharona's sightings will top 600 on the following Monday.

DOTS A LOT (page 11)

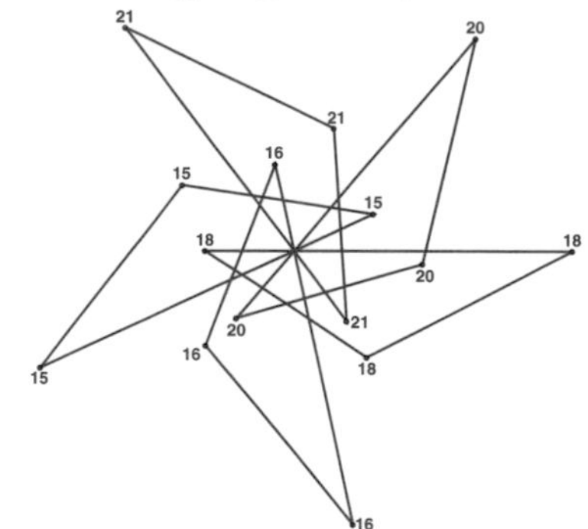

STACKING STANLEY (pages 12-13)

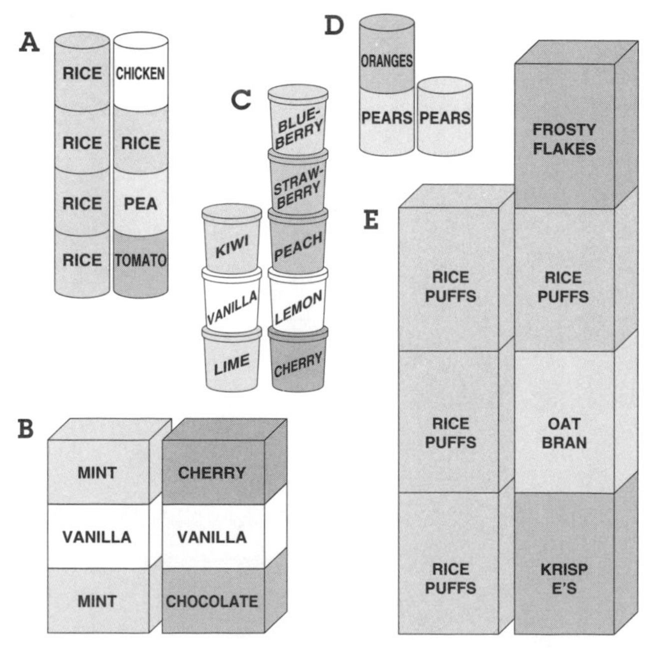

CASTLE CALCULATIONS (page 14)

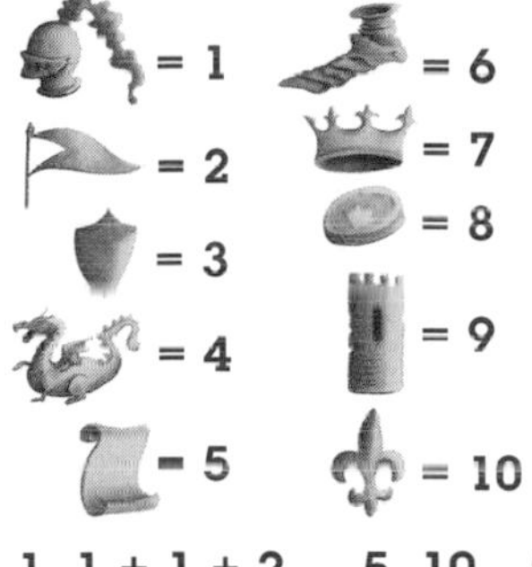

1. $1 + 1 + 2$
2. $2 \times 2 = 4$
3. $8 - 4 = 4$
4. $3 + 3 = 6$
5. $10 - 9 = 1$
6. $2 \times 5 = 10$
7. $8 + 2 = 10$
8. $7 - 6 = 1$

Where did King Arthur learn to use his lance a lot?
IN KNIGHT SCHOOL

SUM SUIT (page 15)

Jacket: $75
Skirt: $50
Vest: $25
TOTAL COST: $150

PARTY PUZZLE (pages 16-17)

July 10

TRICKY QUICKIES (page 18)

A. NINE B. 1

SAND ART (page 19)

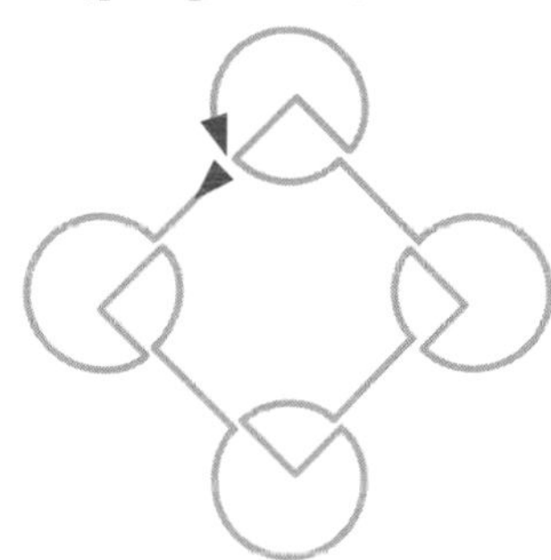

SCRAMBLED PICTURE (pages 20-21)

WHO AM I? (page 22)

1. 22 2. 33 3. 11 4. 222
5. 124 6. 100 7. 444 8. 97531

SUBTRACTION SEQUENCES (page 23)

Why did the octopus always laugh at the number after nine?
TEN TICKLES (Tentacles)

DIGIT DOES IT (pages 24-25)

Dear Inspector Digit,
Please register these 23 stamps, which I trust you will return. When they are delivered to the court, another crook will be canceled. Post Mark

a-3	e-15	k-4	o-16	t-21	y-20
b-6	g-18	l-8	p-1	u-11	
c-9	h-7	m-10	r-5	v-13	
d-12	i-2	n-14	s-19	w-17	

CERTAIN CIRCLES (pages 26-27)

SCHOOL	LINCOLN AVENUE
1. 100	1. 384
2. 36	2. 132
3. 20	3. 155
4. 51	4. 53
5. 25	5. 102
6. 3	6. 282
7. 0	
8. 309	

MATHMAGIC (page 28)

There's a lot to do in this trick, but your friends do all the work. You, as the magician, have it easy. When you glance at the paper to make sure they filled out the chart correctly, look at the number under the 7. Multiply that number by 11, and you'll have the same answer your friends get from totaling the ten numbers. Though your friends chose a number between 1 and 10 to get started, this trick will work using any number.

EQUAL TIME (page 29)

A. $3 + 9 = 17 - 5$
B. $2 \times 7 = 8 + 6$
C. $16 - 8 = 14 - 6$
D. $18 \div 3 = 2 + 4$
E. $6 \times 3 = 9 + 9$
F. $10 + 6 = 9 + 7$
G. $4 \div 4 = 9 - 8$
H. $15 - 8 = 21 \div 3$
I. $3 + 1 = 24 \div 6$
J. $17 - 9 = 1 \times 8$

HOWDY, PARTNERS! (pages 30-31)

BUS BUDDIES (page 32)

Hector, Megan, Amber, and Shaniece will need to ride the bus.

MEASURE UP (page 33)

Here is how Emma measured each inch. You may have used a different method.

1 inch: from 2 to 3
2 inches: from 0 to 2
3 inches: from 0 to 3 or 9 to 12
4 inches: from 8 to 12
5 inches: from 3 to 8
6 inches: from 2 to 8 or 3 to 9
7 inches: from 2 to 9
8 inches: from 0 to 8 or 3 to 11
9 inches: from 0 to 9 or 2 to 11
10 inches: from 2 to 12
11 inches: from 0 to 11
12 inches: from 0 to 12

PAPER PUNCH (pages 34-35)

A. 3 E. 5
B. 7 F. 8
C. 1 G. 6
D. 2 H. 4

WHAT'S THE DIFFERENCE? (page 36)

	MARIA	MARK	DIFFERENCE
Cookie jar	$19.95	$14.50	MARIA paid $5.45 more.
Sweater	$12.00	$23.75	MARK paid $11.75 more.
CD player	$84.39	$79.99	MARIA paid $4.40 more.
Rocking chair	$158.14	$132.23	MARIA paid $25.91 more.
Cat food	$9.48	$14.62	MARK paid $5.14 more.
Clock	$21.81	$27.17	MARK paid $5.36 more.

Overall, Mark paid $292.26. Maria paid $305.77. Mark was the better shopper.

GETTING AROUND (page 37)

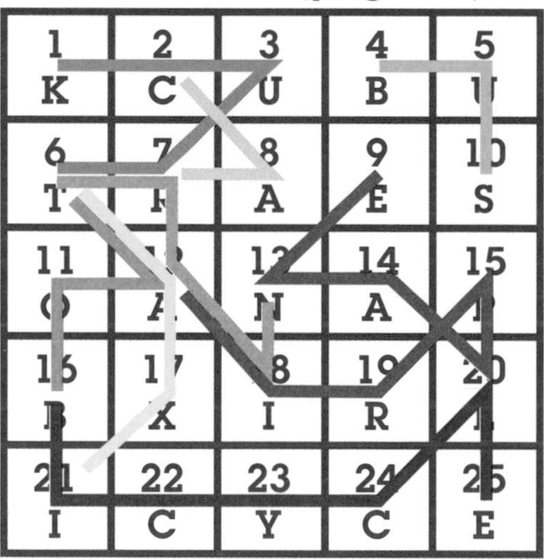

SWEET STUFF (pages 38-39)

	1894	1896	1907	1920	1921	1923	1932	1947
Almond Joy	x	x	x	x	x	x	x	o
Baby Ruth	x	x	x	x	o	x	x	x
Cracker Jack	x	o	x	x	x	x	x	x
Hershey Bar	o	x	x	x	x	x	x	x
Hershey's Kisses	x	x	o	x	x	x	x	x
M&M's	x	x	x	o	x	x	x	x
Milky Way	x	x	x	x	x	o	x	x
3 Musketeers	x	x	x	x	x	x	o	x